sasol

FIRST FIEL[D GUIDE TO] ALOES OF SOUTHERN AFRICA

Aloe spicata (page 47)

loe comptonii (page 22)

GIDEON SMITH

Contents

Aloe excelsa (page 26)

Struik Publishers
(a division of New Holland Publishing (South Africa) (Pty) Ltd)
80 McKenzie Street, Cape Town, 8001 South Africa

New Holland Publishing is a member of the Johnnic Publishing Group.
www.struik.co.za
Log on to our photographic website **www.imagesofafrica.co.za** for an African experience.

First published in 2003
1 3 5 7 9 10 8 6 4 2

Editor: Katharina von Gerhardt
Designer: Lesley Mitchell

Reproduction by Hirt & Carter Cape (Pty) Ltd,
Printed and bound by CTP Book Printers

ISBN: 1 86872 854 4

Introduction

Aloes come in an astonishing array of different shapes and sizes. They range from the lofty tree aloes, such as *Aloe barberae* and *Aloe dichotoma*, which may reach a height of 20 m, to the tiny white grass aloe, *Aloe albida*, and the miniature *Aloe bowiea* – both barely 100 mm tall. Between these extremes, almost every conceivable combination can be found: single-stemmed trees, dainty or robust shrubs, ground-hugging creepers, and even a few cliff-dwellers that grow vertically downwards. They also vary tremendously in the size, shape and arrangement of their leaves, ranging from massive, broad and boat-shaped to tiny, narrow and grass-like, and from rigidly upright to droopy and dangling. The margins and surfaces of the leaves of some aloes are virtually without teeth, while others have sharp spines along the horny edges, or teeth that may be scattered on the upper and lower surfaces. Not to be outdone, the flowers also differ considerably in shape, arrangement and colour. Those of some species are dainty, bell-shaped and off-white, while others have robust, bright red tubes exuding copious amounts of nectar. The endless combinations in which these characters are expressed serve to make aloes irresistible to collectors, gardeners and horticulturists[G].

More than 500 species of *Aloe* are known in the world – 120 of these species are indigenous[G] to South Africa.

Aloe petricola *will brighten up any garden in winter.*

Characteristics of *Aloe* species

Aloes are generally included in the subfamily Alooideae of the family Asphodelaceae. An alternative point of view is that they, along with their relatives in the look-alike genera *Astroloba*

Not an aloe! Century plants look superficially similar to aloes, but they die after having flowered. Plants in this colony of Agave vivipara *var.* vivipara *are in various growth phases. Some have flowered and are now dying back.*

(star-lobes), *Chortolirion* (kleinaalwyn), *Gasteria* (beestong), and *Haworthia* (kleinaalwyn or rosies), should be treated as belonging to their own family, the Aloaceae. Regardless of which family classification is followed, certain features characterise aloes. The most obvious are:

- Fleshy leaves, even if only very slightly, arranged in dense or sparsely leaved rosettes[G].
- Clusters of tubular flowers arranged on elongated or compacted, often candle-like, inflorescences[G].

Certain unrelated succulent plant species look very much like aloes as they too have their spine-edged, boat-shaped leaves arranged in rosettes[G]. One group in particular, representatives of *Agave*, the Century plants, look very much like aloes, but they are mostly found in the subtropics and deserts of central America, Mexico and the southwestern United States of America. Furthermore, they die after having flowered, while aloes are long-lived and flower repeatedly. One species, the Mexican *Agave americana* (blougaringboom), which is widely grown in South Africa, especially in the arid, karroid areas, is used for the production of a high-quality, tequila-like alcoholic beverage.

Growing aloes

Part of the popularity of aloes among collectors and gardeners can be attributed to the ease with which they can be grown. Aloes are propagated primarily through cuttings and seed. Of these two methods, the establishment of new plants through taking cuttings and planting them is by far the most popular. Shrubby and tree-like species, in particular, are propagated in this way. All that needs to be done is to remove a side-branch or basal sprout with a sharp knife and allow the wound to dry off for a few days, after which it can be planted in a well-drained friable soil mixture in a container, or directly in the ground. The cut end can be dipped into commercially available root hormone powder to enhance the formation of roots.

Alternatively, aloes can be grown from seed. This method is very rewarding, as, with the exception of a very few species, aloes are particularly easy to grow from freshly harvested seed. Seed should be spread evenly on the surface of a well-drained soil mixture containing about one part coarse river sand, one part sifted compost and one part loamy garden soil. Cover seed with a thin layer of small pebbles and water thoroughly from the bottom by standing the seedling tray in a shallow container filled with water, so as not to disturb the seeds. If the soil is kept moist, tiny seedlings should emerge within a matter of days. After germination, the seedlings will benefit from a drenching with water to which a fungicide should be added. This will control fungal attacks, which often occur in aloe seedlings. Once their root systems are strong enough, usually within a few months, the seedlings can be transplanted into larger containers or garden beds. A modern trend in domestic and even corporate gardening practices is to use a large variety of plants that are low maintenance, yield a high return in terms of flower colour, attract wildlife to the garden, are hardy (i.e. waterwise) and highly architectural. Aloes satisfy all these requirements. In addition, they combine well with a variety of exotic species popular in gardening. When combined with other South African species, such as strelitzia, agapanthus, clivia, plumbago, pelargoniums and asparagus, aloes are shown to best effect.

Pests and diseases

As is the case with all southern African plants, indigenous[G] pests and parasites affect aloe plants. Fortunately it is comparatively easy to control most of the insect infestations that are normally found on aloes. Arguably the most severe and destructive aloe pest is the aloe snout beetle that burrows into the crown of the rosette[G] where it lays its eggs. Once these hatch, the grubs burrow into the stems, which slowly deteriorate until the

In landscaping, aloes such as Aloe ferox *(foreground) and* Aloe arborescens *(left background) combine perfectly with rocks and other indigenous*[G] *plants, for example* Crassula ovata *(ball-shaped shrubs with pinkish flowers).*

plant finally collapses into a heap. Small holes can be drilled into the stems of large plants and neat systematic insecticide can be injected into these as a *preventative* measure. A systematic, also referred to as a systemic, insecticide, is one that is absorbed into the juices of the plant. However, once a plant has been infested by snout beetles, it is almost certain to die. Another potential problem is aloe cancer, caused by a mite infestation that results in an unnatural proliferation of cells, causing very unsightly growth. Infected parts can be removed and the wound then treated with a powder insecticide. Apart from these two pests, the most frequently encountered problems are the unsightly occurrence of white or brown scale insects on the leaves of aloes, and aphids on their leaves or roots. These pests are easily treated with systematic insecticides that are absorbed by the plant, so poisoning the scale insects through the sap they ingest. Alternatively the leaves should be sprayed with a systematic insecticide to which a wetting agent such as domestic dishwashing liquid has been added.

Conservation of aloes

With very few exceptions, all species of *Aloe* are protected in South Africa. It is illegal to remove aloes from their natural habitat without appropriate permits and the permission of the landowner. Regardless of these protective measures that have been in place for some years, a number of species have become threatened through illegal collecting, urban and industrial expansion and unsound farming practices. No matter how strong the urge to collect plants for your garden from the wild, please observe the laws that are in place to protect aloes. **Remember that extinction is for keeps.** Alternative sources of plants are nurseries that stock aloes, where purchase of aloes is legal, and will not impact on their natural distribution.

How to use this book

In this book a selection of 46 species of *Aloe* is introduced to the reader. Forty-four of these species are indigenous[G] to the subcontinent, while the other two – the Arabian *Aloe vera* and the Ethiopian *Aloe camperi* – are aliens and are widely cultivated in southern Africa. In terms of growth form, a wide range of species is included. The species are arranged alphabetically according to scientific name.

The spiral aloe, Aloe polyphylla, *is the national flower of Lesotho, but threatened in its natural habitat, mainly as a result of illegal collecting.*

Where available, common names are provided. Although often very descriptive, these names can be misleading. Frequently the same common name is in use for a number of different species. For each species information is given on its general characteristics, flower colour, flowering season, natural distribution range (including a thumbnail map), and some interesting facts under a heading for notes. The conservation status of threatened species is also given. The Red Data List categories in which they are included are defined as follows:

Critically Endangered (CR) – the species faces an extremely high risk of becoming extinct in the wild in the immediate future.

Endangered (E) – the species faces a very high risk of becoming extinct in the wild in the near future.

Vulnerable (VU) – the species faces a high risk of becoming extinct in the wild in the medium-term future.

Flower and rosette types

***Raceme*[G]*. This single, cone-shaped raceme*[G] *belongs to* Aloe arborescens.

***Head-shaped raceme*[G]*. The apically flattened raceme*[G] *of* Aloe maculata.

***Branched or compound raceme*[G]*. This inflorescence*[G] *consists of a number of racemes*[G] *and belongs to* Aloe reynoldsii.

Some species of Aloe, *such as* Aloe aculeata, *produce* ***stemless rosettes***[G].

Other species, including Aloe littoralis, *grow as* ***single-stemmed trees*** *that have their trunks clothed in the remains of dried leaves.*

Flowering sequence, from **buds** *(top) to* ***mature female-phase flowers*** *(bottom) of* Aloe pretoriensis. *The flower stalks (***pedicels***[G]*) are supported by small, leaf-like floral* **bracts**[G]. *The* **stamens**[G] *(yellow stalk-like structures) extend beyond the mouth of a flower.*

White-thorn aloe

Aloe aculeata

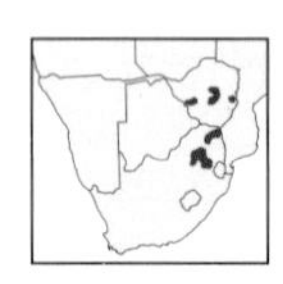

Afrikaans names: knoppies-aalwyn, witdoring-aalwyn

Characteristics: Plants are medium-sized and stemless. Leaves are borne erectly, with their terminal portions curved inwards, especially during the dry season. The leaf margins bear short, stiff, reddish-brown teeth. Leaf surfaces are adorned with numerous scattered teeth that arise from prominent white protuberances, giving the plants a characteristic spotted appearance. Inflorescences[G] are of medium height and can consist of up to four racemes[G].

Flower colour: Buds are reddish orange while flowers are yellow-orange (buds are always a more intense colour than open flowers).

Flowering time: Early to mid-winter.

Distribution: In South Africa, this species occurs in the southern and central parts of the Limpopo Province, as well as in the central northern part of Mpumalanga; it also occurs in Zimbabwe.

Notes: *Aloe aculeata* was featured on the old 10 cent coin of the Republic of South Africa. This is a beautiful plant that warrants being cultivated more frequently, specifically in frost-free, summer-rainfall areas. Especially when in flower, the tall, brightly coloured, candle[G]-like inflorescences[G] light up a drab winter landscape.

Uitenhage aloe

Aloe africana

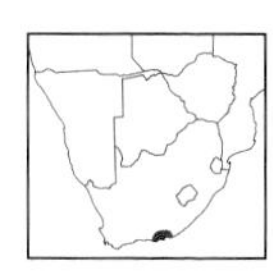

Afrikaans name: Uitenhaagseaalwyn

Characteristics: Plants have a single trunk, but can branch higher up to form tall, sturdy, shrub-like plants. Leaves are strongly and haphazardly curved downward, giving rise to untidy rosettes[G]. Leaf margins bear sharp-tipped, brownish teeth. The stems are covered with the remains of dried leaves. Up to four tall, slender, cone-shaped racemes[G] are borne successively from a single plant. The terminal portions of open flowers are curved upwards.

Flower colour: Buds range from light to deep orange, while open flowers are yellow.

Flowering time: Mostly mid- to late winter, and spring.

Distribution: This is an Eastern Cape aloe, with a distribution range that straddles the area between the Gamtoos River in the west and Port Alfred in the east.

Notes: This is the perfect plant for subtropical coastal gardens. It grows very well in containers and in the open. This species is a real horticultural[G] gem as it tends to flower beyond its principal flowering period.

Skirt aloe

Aloe alooides

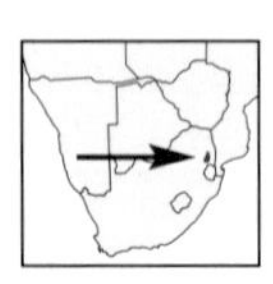

Afrikaans name: rokaalwyn

Characteristics: Plants are robust and single-stemmed. Old specimens can reach a height of three metres. The deeply channelled leaves are very long and strongly down-curved, stretching from the tip of the crown to ground level. This creates the impression that the stems are clothed in a dense skirt of leaves. The leaf edges are adorned with small reddish teeth. The tall flowering stems are covered with small yellow flowers.

Flower colour: Buds are typically greenish while the open flowers are yellow.

Flowering time: Late winter.

Distribution: The species has a limited distribution range, and is restricted to Graskop, Sabie and Nelspruit in Mpumalanga.

Notes: This is a very striking, majestic plant once it reaches maturity. It does well in cultivation, even when grown outside of its natural distribution range. However, it appears to favour mild environmental conditions as found in the Mpumalanga Lowveld.

Krantz aloe

Aloe arborescens

Afrikaans name: kransaalwyn

Characteristics: Plants can be variable in all characters. Leaf colour varies tremendously, from bluish grey to a bright, light green. These multi-headed shrubs range from dainty to robust. The small or large rosettes[G] are borne at the ends of medium-sized branches that are usually clothed in the remains of dead leaves. The narrow leaves are of medium length and are adorned with short, usually whitish or greenish teeth. The conical inflorescences[G], which have one or two branches, are borne near the tips of the rosettes[G]. Individual flowers have a very neat appearance.

Flower colour: Orange, red, pinkish or yellow flowers.

Flowering time: Predominantly early to late winter, but some forms will flower in summer.

Distribution: The species has a wide distribution range, stretching from Cape Point in a continuous range eastwards, through to KwaZulu-Natal and Mpumalanga. It also occurs further afield in Zimbabwe and Malawi.

Notes: This must rate as one of the most useful aloes for gardening and landscaping. It grows very well in almost any situation, and the flowering period can be extended considerably if forms from various parts of its distribution range are grown. As a result of its variability, one can create a garden consisting entirely of the numerous forms of *Aloe arborescens*.

Mossel Bay hybrid[G] aloe

Aloe arborescens x *Aloe ferox*

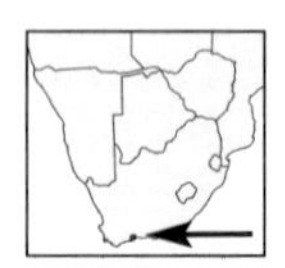

Afrikaans name: basteraalwyn

Characteristics: Plants are variable in the size of their rosettes[G] and flower colour. Generally they grow as large, robust, multi-stemmed shrubs. As in *Aloe ferox*, the stems are usually clothed in the remains of old, dry leaves. Leaves vary from dull bluish green to light green and are borne in strong rosettes[G]. The terminal parts of the leaves are curved downwards. Leaf margins are covered in white teeth. Inflorescences[G] have many branches, consisting of large, erect, densely flowered candles[G].

Flower colour: Ranges from a bright orange to a deep crimson.

Flowering time: Winter.

Distribution: This hybrid[G] occurs around Mossel Bay in the southern Western Cape.

Notes: This is a wonderful hybrid[G], suitable for extensive use in gardens. Plants are strong in cultivation and very pest resistant. It is by far the most commonly grown aloe in the winter-rainfall region of South Africa.

Tree aloe

Aloe barberae

Afrikaans names: mikaalwyn, boomaalwyn

Characteristics: Plants grow as single-stemmed trees that can reach a height of 20 m. The stems and older parts of the branches are covered in a grey bark that bears longitudinal fissures. The main trunk forks into branches higher up, each ending in a small to medium-sized rosette[G] of slender leaves edged with white teeth. Inflorescences[G] are short and usually branched, consisting of two or three cylindrical racemes[G]. Each raceme[G] is covered with thick flowers.

Flower colour: Salmon pink to rosy red or deep orange.

Flowering time: Mid- to late winter.

Distribution: The species occurs in protected pockets in wooded ravines in coastal forests, from East London in the Eastern Cape, north and eastwards through KwaZulu-Natal to Swaziland and Mpumalanga.

Notes: The species can be grown from branches or cuttings. It can tolerate a wide range of environmental conditions and will easily survive frosts, especially if the plants are mature and established. In contrast to most species of *Aloe*, it will also grow quite well in soil with poor drainage.

Coega aloe[CR]

Aloe bowiea

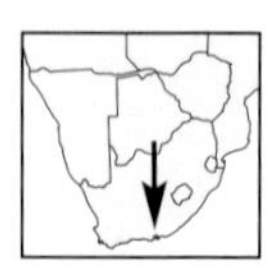

Afrikaans names: kleinaalwyn, Coega-aalwyn

Characteristics: Plants grow as profusely suckering[G], miniature rosettes[G], consisting of leaves that are flattened and broad towards their bases. Towards the tips, they become thin and grass-like. Plants can form large mats with a diameter of 50 centimetres. The green leaves have white spots. Leaf margins are adorned with minute, harmless, white teeth. The unbranched inflorescences[G] bear small flowers that are sparsely arranged on the central axis.

Flower colour: Greenish brown with a tinge of yellow.

Flowering time: Spring to summer.

Distribution: The species has a restricted natural distribution range near Coega, Uitenhage and Kirkwood in the Eastern Cape.

Notes: *Aloe bowiea* is highly threatened and a candidate to become the first South African aloe to become extinct in the wild. Every effort should be made to protect it in its natural habitat. Numerous factors are contributing to the demise of this unassuming species, ranging from unsound farming practices such as overgrazing, to industrial development, urbanisation and the spread of alien species.

Branddraai aloe

Aloe branddraaiensis

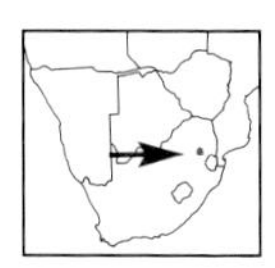

Afrikaans name: Branddraai-aalwyn

Characteristics: Plants are stemless, and form small clumps through sprouting from their bases. The fairly large rosettes[G] consist of numerous leaves that become distinctly tinged with red when growing in the open. Leaves are lined with longitudinal, whitish stripes and are spotted with numerous H-shaped, white flecks. Leaf margins are armed with sharp, brown teeth. The inflorescences[G] have numerous branches, and each raceme[G] carries a head-shaped cluster of basally inflated flowers.

Flower colour: Deep red.

Flowering time: Mid-winter.

Distribution: The species has a restricted distribution range in Mpumalanga, near Branddraai.

Notes: With its reddish, lined leaves and large, branched and re-branched inflorescences[G], this is one of the more beautiful spotted aloes. A single plant can carry more than 50 racemes[G] at the same time – a truly spectacular sight. Although its distribution range is quite restricted, it is exceptionally common around the small town of Branddraai.

Burgersfort aloe

Aloe burgersfortensis

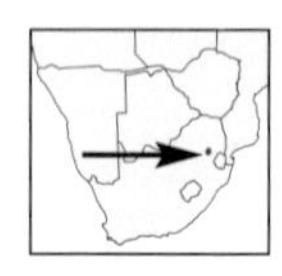

Afrikaans name: Burgersfort-bontaalwyn

Characteristics: Plants grow as low rosettes[G], sprouting new plants from the base to form small clumps with time. The rosettes[G] are flattened, giving them an open appearance. The brownish-green leaves are faintly lined and adorned with large, scattered H-shaped, creamy white flecks. Leaf margins are armed with short, sharp, brown teeth. Flowers are basally inflated. Inflorescences[G] have many dense branches, but are sparsely flowered. Individual racemes[G] are elongated and more or less cylindrical.

Flower colour: A dull red, with white stripes along the length of the flowers.

Flowering time: Mid-winter.

Distribution: The species mainly occurs around the towns of Burgersfort, Steelpoort and near Barberton.

Notes: The densest concentration of different *Aloe* species is around the Mpumalanga town of Burgersfort, after which this species was named. A fairly large number of spotted and other aloes occur in the vicinity of this town.

Camper's aloe

Aloe camperi

Afrikaans name: groenaalwyn

Characteristics: Plants are low-growing shrubs that branch from the base. Their stems are erect or creeping and can reach a length of one metre. The fairly long leaves are crowded along the stems, recurved or horizontal, and faintly spotted with white or light greenish flecks, especially towards the base. Leaf margins are armed with short, stiff, brownish-green teeth. An inflorescence[G] has up to eight branches, each carrying a short, cylindrical raceme[G] that is densely covered with small, club-shaped flowers.

Flower colour: Varies from yellow and orange (common) to reddish orange. Buds are usually reddish, while the open flowers are yellow, giving inflorescences[G] a bi-coloured appearance.

Flowering time: Early to mid-summer.

Distribution: The species is indigenous[G] to Ethiopia and Eritrea, but is very widely grown in South Africa in public and private gardens. It even has an Afrikaans common name!

Notes: A striking form of this aloe has intensely orange-yellow flowers. Interestingly, the teeth on the leaf margins of some forms of this species appear to be extensions of the leaf blades, unlike those of some species of *Aloe* that are carried on reddish ridges.

Cat's-tail aloe

Aloe castanea

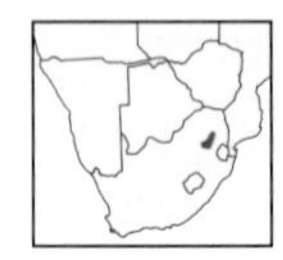

Afrikaans name: katstertaalwyn

Characteristics: Plants are small to medium-sized shrubby trees that consist of a few robust branches arising from a very short main trunk. Each branch supports a large, open rosette[G], which consists of erect, dull yellowish-green leaves and is covered with the remains of dried leaves. The elongated, twisted inflorescences[G] are densely flowered. Flowers are surprisingly small and filled with dark brown nectar.

Flower colour: Deep brown; the conspicuous stamens[G] are an intense orange-red.

Flowering time: Winter.

Distribution: The distribution range straddles the border where the Limpopo, Mpumalanga and Gauteng provinces meet.

Notes: This is a beautiful, very hardy aloe that warrants being cultivated more often, particularly in Highveld gardens. Copious amounts of nectar are produced by the flowers, and act as a perfect attractant of sunbirds to a garden.

Grey aloe

Aloe chabaudii var. *chabaudii*

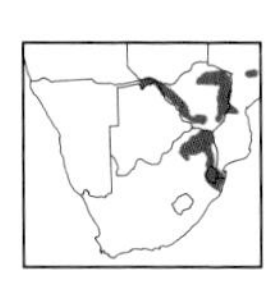

Afrikaans name: grysaalwyn

Characteristics: Plants grow as small, tufted shrubs that form dense colonies through basal suckers[G]. Each rosette[G] consists of erect leaves, the terminal parts of which may be slightly outwardly curved to produce neat, open rosettes[G]. The narrow leaves are a greyish-green colour that turns pinkish grey during times of drought. Inflorescences[G] usually have many branches, and a mature plant will produce two or three inflorescences[G] simultaneously or successively. The bow-shaped flowers are sparsely arranged in head-shaped or elongated, conical racemes[G].

Flower colour: Dull pinkish to coral red. Bi-coloured specimens, combining red tubes with yellowish mouths, are known to occur.

Flowering time: Mid- to late winter.

Distribution: It occurs widely in the northeastern parts of South Africa, especially in the Limpopo and Mpumalanga provinces and also in neighbouring countries to the north.

Notes: A delightful species in cultivation, and its nectar-rich flowers will attract sunbirds and insect life to any garden. Unlike many other *Aloe* species, *Aloe chabaudii* will happily grow in the deep shade of shrubs and trees.

Compton's aloe

Aloe comptonii

Afrikaans name: Kleinkaroo-aalwyn

Characteristics: Plants are stemless, yet may develop short stems that creep along the ground, but the rosettes[G] are turned upwards. Rosettes[G] consist of a fair number of erect leaves that are a distinct bluish green. Leaf margins are sparingly armed with short, stout, white teeth. Inflorescences[G] have numerous branches, each carrying a head-shaped raceme[G]. The pencil-shaped flowers are densely packed in tight clusters at the tips of the racemes[G].

Flower colour: Red, varying from a fairly dull shade of pink to very bright crimson.

Flowering time: Spring and summer.

Distribution: A wide distribution in the southern Cape, particularly in the Little Karoo, straddling the border between the Western and Eastern Cape.

Notes: *Aloe comptonii* is very easy to cultivate and a worthwhile addition to any garden as it provides bright colour in early spring and summer months. In its natural habitat, plants form dense colonies.

Yellow aloe

Aloe cryptopoda

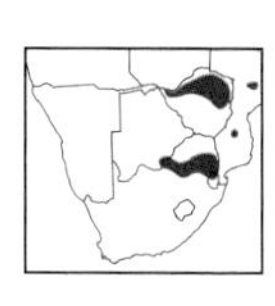

Afrikaans name: geelaalwyn

Characteristics: Plants are stemless and unbranched, producing large rosettes[G] of distinctly yellowish-green leaves. Leaves are borne erectly and tend to curve inwards, over-arching the centre of the rosettes[G], especially in times of drought. Leaf margins are armed with small, sharp, reddish-brown teeth. The inflorescences[G] are branched into numerous racemes[G], each of these bearing a terminal cluster of flowers. The racemes[G] are distinctly cone-shaped.

Flower colour: Flower buds are uniformly red, while open flowers turn yellowish and their tips tend to become greenish. However, the inflorescences[G] are not bi-coloured.

Flowering time: Some variation, but it flowers mostly in mid-winter.

Distribution: The species occurs in a broad east-west band in the southern parts of the Limpopo Province. It extends into Botswana, Gauteng, Mpumalanga and Swaziland, and has also been recorded in Mozambique and in central and northern Zimbabwe.

Notes: *Aloe cryptopoda*, a typical bushveld (savanna) species, is a very useful garden subject in frost-free, summer-rainfall areas. It is especially striking when in flower.

Quiver tree

Aloe dichotoma

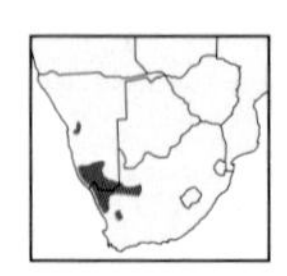

Afrikaans name: kokerboom

Characteristics: These plants have massive, unbranched stems that support dense canopies of robust, forked branches. Old specimens may have the shape of an inverted cone. The bark on the central stem is smooth in sections, but splits longitudinally, giving it a ridged appearance. Each branch carries a small crown of greyish-green leaves that are armed with short, whitish teeth. Leaves are shed once dry. The short inflorescences[G] hardly protrude above the canopy.

Flower colour: Butter-yellow.

Flowering time: Mid- to late winter.

Distribution: The species occurs in a west-east band from the Richtersveld through Namaqualand and Bushmanland in the Northern Cape, and also in Namibia.

Notes: This aloe is a majestic plant when mature, but even when young the tiered arrangement of leaves makes it a striking plant for arid gardens. The common name is derived from the fact that the San used the hollowed-out stems as quivers for arrows. If the 'Big Five' plant species of South Africa were to be chosen, the kokerboom would surely be one of them.

Grass aloe

Aloe ecklonis

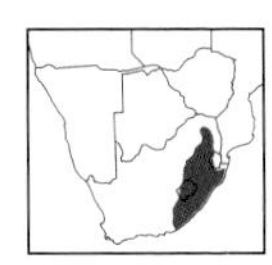

Afrikaans name: groot-grasaalwyn

Characteristics: Plants grow as large, robust tufts of multi-headed rosettes[G]. The thin and slightly succulent leaves are broader than those of most species of grass aloe. Leaf blades are uniformly dull green. The undersides of the leaf bases of some forms can be covered in dense white spots. Leaf margins are adorned with firm, white, but harmless teeth. The unbranched inflorescences[G] bear dense clusters of large, tubular flowers in head-shaped rosettes[G].

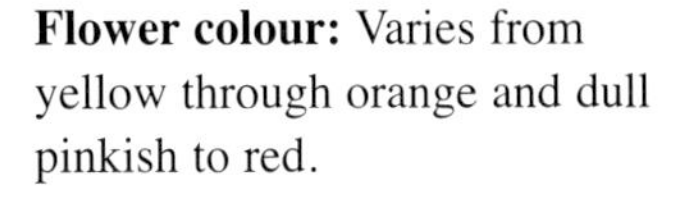

Flower colour: Varies from yellow through orange and dull pinkish to red.

Flowering time: Mid-summer.

Distribution: The species is widely distributed through the grasslands of the eastern parts of South Africa and Lesotho.

Notes: The thin, flat leaves are a misleading feature of this grass aloe – however, once the species flowers it is an unmistakable grass aloe as a result of, among other characters, its head-shaped flower clusters. Numerous inflorescences[G] can be produced simultaneously or successively by a single plant. These flower clusters almost entirely hide the leaves and make the plants easy to locate when they are in flower.

Zimbabwe aloe

Aloe excelsa

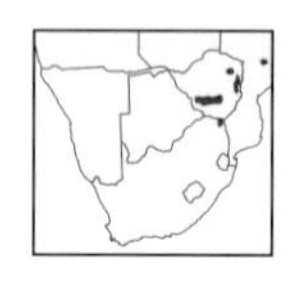

Afrikaans name: Zimbabwe-aalwyn

Characteristics: Plants are very tall and slender, and can reach heights of four metres. They grow as unbranched, single-stemmed specimens. The stems are protected by a skirt of dry leaves. The fairly long leaves are narrowly boat-shaped, and erect, or sometimes recurved, in the upper third section. Leaves carry scattered teeth on both surfaces and are deeply channelled. The leaf margins are armed with sharp, brownish teeth. Inflorescences[G] are divided into a number of erect to slightly horizontal branches, except in very young plants where the inflorescence[G] usually consists of a single raceme[G].

Flower colour: Dark red to deep orange. Yellow at times.

Flowering time: Late winter to spring.

Distribution: In South Africa the species is restricted to the north-eastern corner of the Limpopo Province, but it is more widely distributed in Zimbabwe.

Notes: *Aloe excelsa* is a typical bushveld aloe. Along with *Aloe marlothii*, it is one of the few South African aloes that has its flowers slanted vertically on racemes[G] that are borne at an angle (rather than vertically). However, *Aloe excelsa* can be distinguished from *Aloe marlothii* by being a more slender plant.

Bitter aloe

Aloe ferox

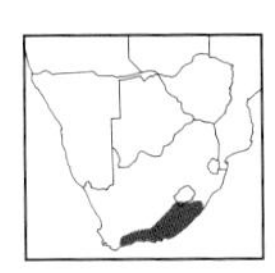

Afrikaans names: bitteraalwyn, Karoo-aalwyn

Distribution: The species has a wide east-west distribution – from near Pietermaritzburg in the east to Riversdale in the west.

Characteristics: Plants can reach a height of up to five metres – they are robust and grow as unbranched, single-stemmed specimens. The stems are always protected by a scraggly skirt of persistent, dry leaves. Leaves can be long and erect or recurved in their upper halves. Although the leaves are usually smooth, some forms may bear scattered teeth on both surfaces. Leaf margins are armed with sharp, brownish teeth. The tall, cylindrical, candelabra-like inflorescences[G] have numerous branches.

Flower colour: Red, orange, yellow or, rarely, white.

Flowering time: Usually winter, although specimens from very cold areas tend to flower later, in spring or even in summer.

Notes: One of the most spectacular of all aloes in cultivation – it grows quickly and will flower within a few years. Plants are quite frost and pest resistant.
It is also the source of a dried crystalline brown product called 'Cape aloes'. This substance is taken neat for stomach ailments.

Scrambling aloe

Aloe gracilis

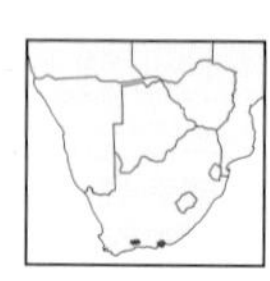

Afrikaans name: rankaalwyn

Characteristics: Plants grow as large, dense shrubs, and their stems often become entangled by the surrounding plants. The long stems, which arise from strong, thick roots, are thin but able to support themselves. Only in some forms do the stems sprawl along the ground. The leaves are widely spaced along the stems and tend to die off from the bottom of the stem upwards. Inflorescences[G] are fairly short, with large, slightly curved flowers sparsely arranged on the central axis.

Flower colour: Bright red, but open mouths are yellowish.

Flowering time: Mid-winter to early summer.

Distribution: Occurs near Port Elizabeth in the Eastern Cape, and further westwards on the Langeberg in the Western Cape.

Notes: *Aloe gracilis* is the delight of any gardener. The plants grow very easily and flower profusely. Unlike most other scrambling aloes, its main flowering time, winter, coincides with that of most aloes. Although the parts of the plant that grow above the ground are susceptible to the cold, stems regenerate from the thick rootstock every spring.

Kleinbontaalwyn

Aloe grandidentata

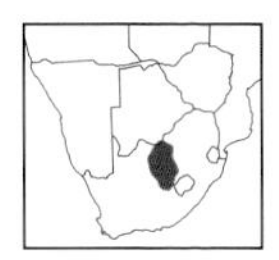

Afrikaans name: aanteelaalwyn, kanniedood

Characteristics: Plants are fairly small, but multiply profusely to form large clumps. The small, triangular leaves are very thick and succulent and armed with sharp marginal teeth. Leaves are beautifully spotted with H-shaped, white flecks. The inflorescences[G] are branched into two or more racemes[G]. A distinguishing feature of this species is its club-shaped flowers, which lack the basal swelling of the flowers of most spotted *Aloe* species.

Flower colour: Pinkish red.

Flowering time: Late winter to spring.

Distribution: Occurs in a north-south band in the climatically severe central parts of South Africa, around Kimberley for example. Its distribution range also extends into Botswana.

Notes: This species can tolerate extreme environmental conditions. It serves as a useful groundcover. It is one of very few South African *Aloe* species that has club-shaped flowers.

Spotted aloe

Aloe greatheadii var. *davyana*

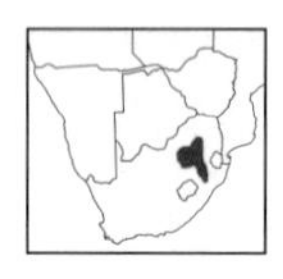

Afrikaans names: bontaalwyn, kleinaalwyn

Characteristics: Plants are small and solitary, but may occasionally branch to form small, tightly packed clumps. The brown-green leaves are very thick, nearly triangular in outline and armed with sharp, pungent, brownish teeth. The upper leaf surfaces are mottled with H-shaped white flecks, while the lower surfaces are uniformly dull green. Each rosette[G] produces a medium to tall and multi-branched inflorescence[G].

Flower colour: Red to dull pink, with white longitudinal stripes.

Flowering time: Early to late winter.

Distribution: The species occurs above the climatically severe inland escarpment of South Africa. It is the common winter-flowering spotted aloe that occurs on the Witwatersrand and between Pretoria and Johannesburg.

Notes: When established *en masse*, plants produce a striking display of pinkish-red flowers in winter. Beekeepers also find this a very useful species as the plants flower profusely in winter, when most of the other plants that share its natural distribution range are dormant. The soothing leaf juices of *Aloe greatheadii* var. *davyana* are applied to blisters, sores and insect bites.

Sand aloe

Aloe hereroensis var. *hereroensis*

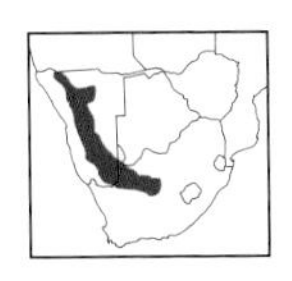

Afrikaans names: sandaalwyn, deurmekaarkoppie, vlakteaalwyn

Characteristics: Plants are stemless and usually grow singly, or more rarely, as once- or twice-branched clumps. The lower surfaces of the brownish-grey leaves are faintly to distinctly lined and spotted with H-shaped, white flecks. Leaf margins are armed with sharp, reddish-brown teeth. The inflorescences[G] have many branches consisting of numerous head-shaped racemes[G]. Racemes[G] consist of dense flower clusters that are wider than they are long. The mouths of the flowers are typically upturned.

Flower colour: Ranges from bright red and orange to yellow. However, flowers are typically uniform in colour.

Flowering time: Mid-winter to spring.

Distribution: A species with a wide distribution range in the central-northern parts of the Northern Cape, particularly in areas with sandy soils. It also occurs in Namibia.

Notes: A beautiful species that is best left in its natural habitat. It does not do well on South Africa's Highveld region, where it is inhibited by high summer rainfall.

Spotted aloe

Aloe immaculata

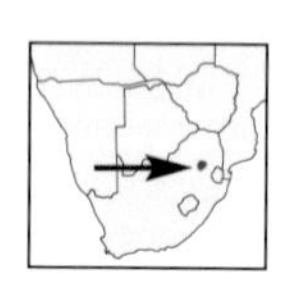

Afrikaans name: bontaalwyn

Characteristics: Plants occur mostly singly – only very rarely are suckering[G] plants encountered. The leaves are coppery green in colour and their upper surfaces carry scattered, H-shaped, whitish flecks, while the lower surfaces are usually uniform in colour. Leaf margins are armed with numerous, densely packed, sharp, brown teeth. The heavily branched inflorescences[G] consist of numerous cone-shaped racemes[G]. Flowers have the distinctive basal swellings typical of spotted aloes.

Flower colour: Varies from a dull, pinkish red to crimson.

Flowering time: Mid- to late winter.

Distribution: The species is common in the Limpopo Province, southwards from Polokwane to Lydenburg.

Notes: Spotted aloes generally do not feature among the top ten species on the 'wanted list' of gardeners, and even to collectors they usually have little more than novelty value. The reason is simple: they are not the most striking species of Aloe, and *Aloe immaculata* is a case in point.

Limpopo spotted aloe

Aloe longibracteata

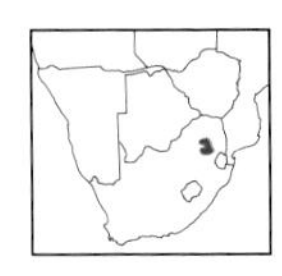

Afrikaans name: Limpopo-bontaalwyn

Characteristics: Plants form small, solitary, low-growing rosettes[G]. Clumps are never formed and plants do not produce suckers[G]. The thick leaves are succulent and triangular in outline. Their triangular shape is enhanced as the leaves die back from their tips. The upper leaf surfaces are densely spotted with oval-shaped, white blotches that often unite in bands. The lower surfaces are pale green and unspotted. Leaf margins carry sharp, brown teeth. The heavily branched inflorescences[G] are fairly tall for such a low-growing plant. Flowers are supported by long bracts[G] and have basal swellings typical of the flowers of spotted aloes.

Flower colour: Varies from deep pink to bright orange-red, and the flowers often have yellow tips.

Flowering time: Mid- to late winter.

Distribution: This *Aloe* species occurs in scattered colonies in the central areas of the Limpopo Province and in north-central Mpumalanga. It is common near Polokwane, Middelburg and Lydenburg.

Notes: This is one of the few species of spotted aloe that never forms large colonies through suckering[G]. Although *Aloe longibracteata* is often included in *Aloe greatheadii* var. *davyana*, it is retained here as a separate species. Interestingly, the racemes[G] tend not to curve away from the main axis as is most often the case in spotted aloes.

Spotted aloe hybrid[G]

Aloe maculata x *Aloe striata*

Afrikaans name: mak-bontaalwyn

Characteristics: Plants grow as sparingly branched, stemless rosettes[G] that sucker[G] freely. The neat rosettes[G] are medium-sized. The leaves are a dull blue-green, like those of *Aloe striata*, and spotted with H-shaped, white flecks. The shape of the leaves is similar to that of *Aloe maculata*. The leaf margins carry small, white teeth on a prominent pink margin as found in *Aloe striata*. The inflorescences[G] have many branches and consist of a large number of densley or loosely packed flowers that generally lack the bulbous basal swellings found in *Aloe maculata*.

Flower colour: Dull to bright orange.

Flowering time: Late winter.

Distribution: This hybrid[G] is known from gardens only.

Notes: This is a very common hybrid[G] in domestic gardens, and must be one of the most common aloes in cultivation. It grows exceptionally easily and flowers freely. The characters of the plants are remarkably constant given that it is of hybrid[G] origin.

Mountain aloe

Aloe marlothii var. *marlothii*

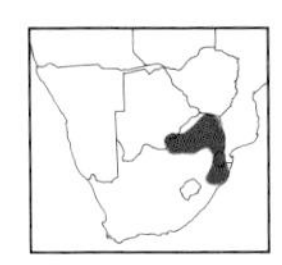

Afrikaans name: bergaalwyn

Characteristics: Plants are large and robust, and grow as unbranched, single-stemmed specimens. They can reach a height of four metres. The stems are protected by a skirt of dry leaves. The long, boat-shaped leaves are usually erect, or sometimes recurved in the upper third section. The leaves bear scattered teeth on both surfaces, but in the case of some forms the surfaces are entirely smooth. Leaf margins are armed with sharp, brownish teeth. Inflorescences[G] are divided into a number of horizontal branches on which flowers are carried in an upright position.

Flower colour: Red, orange or yellow, or a combination thereof.

Flowering time: Winter, or spring in the case of specimens from very cold areas.

Distribution: The species is widely distributed in the inland summer-rainfall regions of South Africa.

Notes: *Aloe marlothii* var. *marlothii* is the northern bushveld equivalent of *Aloe ferox*. It grows exceptionally well in cultivation, even though it is prone to snout beetle attacks. This is one of the few South African aloes that carries its flowers erectly on horizontal side-branches.

Fynbos grass aloe[VU]

Aloe micracantha

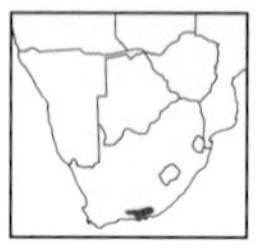

Afrikaans names: fynbosgrasaalwyn, wateraalwyn

Characteristics: Plants grow in small clumps that resemble robust tufts of grass. The thin leaves are borne erectly and have small white spots near their bases. Leaf margins are adorned with soft, harmless, white teeth. Usually only a single raceme[G] arises from each rosette[G]. The flat-topped raceme[G] bears numerous over-sized, hanging flowers in dense clusters.

Flower colour: Bright orange to red.

Flowering time: Mid-summer.

Distribution: *Aloe micracantha* is widely but sparsely distributed in the Eastern Cape, from Uniondale in the west to Grahamstown in the east. It typically grows in grassy fynbos vegetation.

Notes: An interesting feature of this species is the very large, thickened roots that grow horizontally at a shallow depth below the soil surface. In South Africa, it has the most westerly distribution of all grass aloes.

Blue krantz aloe

Aloe mutabilis

Afrikaans names: blou-kransaalwyn, kransaalwyn

Characteristics: Plants are large and single-stemmed, but can grow as branched, short-stemmed shrubs. They often occur on cliff faces. Rosettes[G] are large and open, and appear somewhat flattened. The soft, blue-green leaves are quite long and twisted. Leaf margins are armed with solid, yellowish teeth. The inflorescences[G] have one or two branches and consist of short, often bi-coloured, racemes[G].

Flower colour: Flower buds are red, while the open flowers are yellow. Forms with uniformly red flowers may be encountered.

Flowering time: Mid-winter.

Distribution: The species occurs from Johannesburg in the south to the vicinity of Polokwane in the Limpopo Province in the north, and in an east-west band along the Magaliesberg.

Notes: This species can be confused with *Aloe arborescens*, but is distinguished by its shorter, usually bi-coloured racemes[G], larger, blue-green rosettes[G] and sickle-shaped leaves. It is very easy in cultivation and remarkably cold-resistant and shade-tolerant, but care should be taken that plants are not over-watered.

Purple spotted aloe

Aloe parvibracteata

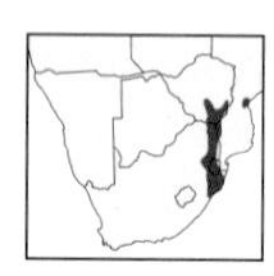

Afrikaans name: pers-bontaalwyn

Characteristics: These extremely variable plants grow as single, stemless rosettes[G] or, more commonly, form large clusters through basal suckers[G]. The leaves are either strongly recurved or spread horizontally and are either bright green with numerous H-shaped white flecks or uniformly purple, with few markings. Leaf margins are consistently armed with sharp, brownish teeth. The tall inflorescences[G] are heavily branched and always erect. The flowers are sparsely arranged on a flowering stem.

Flower colour: Varies from orange to all shades of pink and red.

Flowering time: Mid-winter.

Distribution: Wide distribution in central-northern KwaZulu-Natal, Swaziland and eastern Mpumalanga.

Notes: This is a useful species to grow as a groundcover, as it will rapidly become established in denuded areas or in open beds. Furthermore, it grows very easily. Uniformly purple-leaved plants are by far the most beautiful of the numerous forms available.

Pearson's aloe[E]

Aloe pearsonii

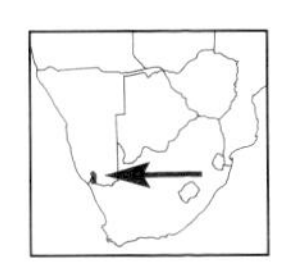

Afrikaans name: struikaalwyn

Characteristics: Plants grow as large, heavily branched shrubs that may reach a height of two metres. The erect stems are clothed in neat rows of triangular leaves that curve strongly downwards. The bottom half of the stems is covered in dry leaves that remain attached to the medium-sized trunks. Leaves are bluish green, but rapidly turn a deep shade of red in times of drought. Leaf margins are armed with short, triangular, white teeth.

Flower colour: Varies from reddish orange to bright yellow.

Flowering time: Mid-summer.

Distribution: The species occurs in the arid mountainous parts of the Richtersveld in the Northern Cape and in southern Namibia.

Notes: This species prefers winter rainfall, and then only very little. *Aloe pearsonii* is not easy in cultivation, and it is best to admire it in its natural state. In its habitat in the arid northwestern parts of the Northern Cape province the species is being threatened by overgrazing, trampling and illegal collecting activities.

Fan aloe

Aloe plicatilis

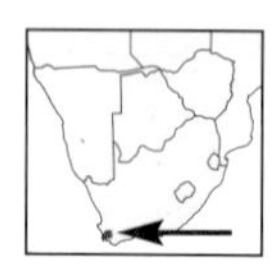

Afrikaans names: waaier-aalwyn, Franschhoekaalwyn

Characteristics: Plants grow as small, heavily branched trees with a short trunk. Stems and older branches are covered with a thick, corky bark that protects it against fires that ravage its natural distribution range. The tongue-shaped leaves have smooth edges. It is one of the very few aloes that has its leaves arranged in the shape of a fan. Inflorescences[G] are short and laxly flowered.

Flower colour: Red to crimson.

Flowering time: Late winter to spring.

Distribution: The species is restricted to a small mountainous area in the Western Cape.

Notes: This is a beautiful plant to grow in winter-rainfall areas. The striking fan-shaped arrangement of its leaves, combined with the sharply tapering flowers makes it a plant well worth growing. It is one of the few *Aloe* species that has fibres in its leaves.

French aloe

Aloe pluridens

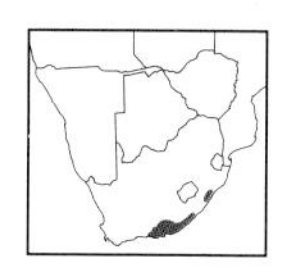

Afrikaans name: Fransaalwyn

Characteristics: Plants are slender and single stemmed, and produce numerous off-sets along the trunks. The upper parts of the stems are covered in the papery remains of dry leaves. The light green leaves are faintly lined and strongly recurved into tight, neat, spiralling rosettes[G]. Leaf margins are adorned with small, whitish teeth. The sparingly branched inflorescences[G] are cone-shaped and carry dense clusters of pencil-shaped flowers.

Flower colour: Bright orange, very rarely yellow.

Flowering time: Winter.

Distribution: The species has a wide distribution in the Eastern Cape, with a few scattered communities further north near Durban in KwaZulu-Natal.

Notes: *Aloe pluridens* is a magnificent species that is easy to grow. It does extremely well in coastal gardens, in containers or in the open ground. The rosettes[G] are always tilted to one side, giving them a lopsided appearance. The species is quite resistant to snout beetle attacks.

Pretoria aloe

Aloe pretoriensis

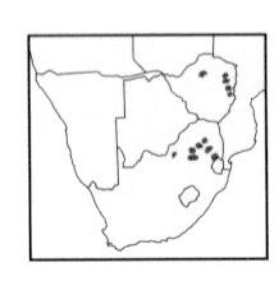

Afrikaans name: Pretoria-aalwyn

Characteristics: Plants are generally solitary and consist of a rosette[G] with dense leaves, which is carried on a short stem that is usually covered in the remains of old leaves. The blue-green leaves are narrow and striped. Leaves tend to die back from the tips, leaving them with long, dry, almost grass-like apices. Leaf margins are armed with sharp teeth. Inflorescences[G] are very tall, branched into a few racemes[G] and cone-shaped. The thin flowers appear pencil-like.

Flower colour: Usually bright red, but reddish-orange forms are occasionally encountered.

Flowering time: Early through mid-winter.

Distribution: The species has a scattered distribution range in Gauteng, Mpumalanga and Limpopo Province and occurs further north in Zimbabwe.

Notes: A magnificent plant when grown successfully, but it can be quite challenging in cultivation in that the plants are prone to cancer infestations. The best characters of the plants are the blue leaves and tall inflorescences[G] bearing bright red flowers.

Powder aloe[VU]

Aloe pruinosa

Afrikaans names: poeieraalwyn, slangkopaalwyn, kleinaalwyn

Characteristics: In contrast to so many spotted aloes, plants are solitary, and suckering[G] only occurs if the growing point is damaged. Both surfaces of the long leaves are densely spotted. On the lower surfaces, the spots often combine to give the surface a milky white sheen. The leaf margins are armed with sharp, triangular teeth. The inflorescence[G] is heavily branched, consisting of numerous sparsely flowered, cylindrical racemes[G].

Flower colour: Dull pinkish, with alternating, longitudinal white stripes.

Flowering time: Late summer.

Distribution: The species has a restricted distribution range around Pietermaritzburg in KwaZulu-Natal.

Notes: Most plant parts (excluding the leaves) growing above the ground are covered in a dense layer of powdery wax. This species is threatened by industrial expansion and urbanisation.

Maiden quiver tree[VU]

Aloe ramosissima

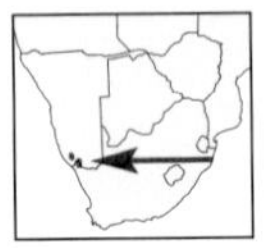

Afrikaans name: nooiens-kokerboom

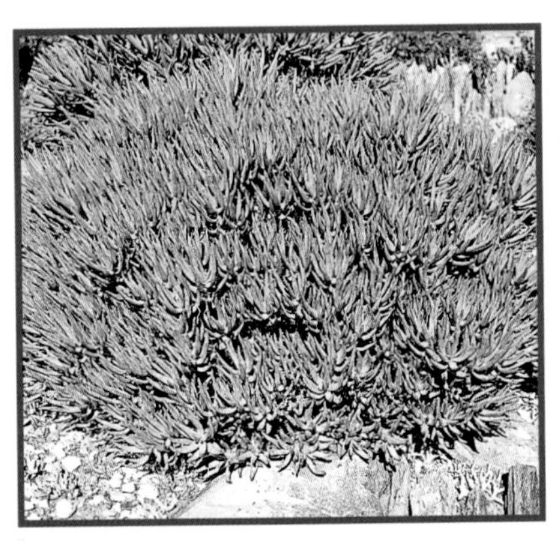

Characteristics: Plants are robust shrubs with large, rounded canopies. A central stem, if present, is very short. The canopy consists of a massive tangle of branches where each branch carries a small cluster of fat, dull grey leaves. The leaf margins are armed with inconspicuous brownish teeth. The thick, fat flowers are borne on short, stout racemes[G].

Flower colour: Bright yellow.

Flowering time: Mid-winter.

Distribution: In South Africa, this species is restricted to the Richtersveld, the arid, northernmost part of the Northern Cape. It also occurs in southern Namibia.

Notes: The large, rounded canopies of mature plants of *Aloe ramosissima* give them a very neat appearance. Well-grown specimens are highly prized as garden specimens. Plants grow better in winter-rainfall areas and protection against summer rain is essential. Although it has been suggested that *Aloe ramosissima* should be regarded as a variety of *Aloe dichotoma*, it is here retained as a separate species.

Bottle-brush aloe

Aloe rupestris

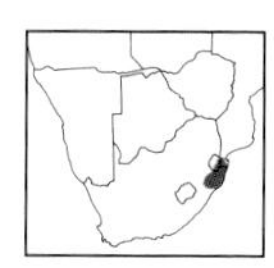

Afrikaans name: kraalaalwyn

Characteristics: Plants are tall and single-stemmed, although they often form small plantlets near the base of the plant. These off-sets usually never reach the same height as the main trunk. The thin leaves are a dark, shiny green colour. Their margins are armed with sharp, brown teeth. The erect inflorescences[G], which are usually heavily branched, are short and cylindrical. The buds and flowers are very tightly packed along the central axis of the individual racemes[G].

Flower colour: Light orange-yellow; stamens[G] are bright red.

Flowering time: Late winter to spring.

Distribution: The species has a wide distribution in the northern KwaZulu-Natal coastal areas. It also occurs in Swaziland and Mozambique.

Notes: This is an archetypal aloe that will make an excellent feature plant in any garden. Although essentially a coastal species, it grows well in more severe climates if given a bit of protection, especially against frost. Unfortunately white scale insects tend to infect leaf surfaces easily. The racemes[G] appear bright red as a result of the prominent stamens[G], which dominate the dull yellowish flowers.

Tilt-head aloe

Aloe speciosa

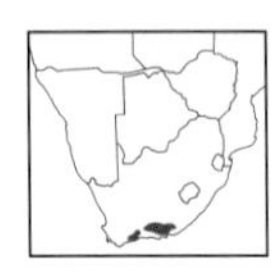

Afrikaans names: Spaansaalwyn, slaphoringaalwyn

Characteristics: Plants grow as single-stemmed or branched trees. Branching occurs low down, from a short trunk. The stems are clothed with the remains of dry leaves. Rosettes[G] are quite large, tilted and consist of leaves that are twisted and turned. The smooth leaves are blue-green with a pinkish tinge. Leaf margins are adorned with small, harmless, reddish teeth. Inflorescences[G] are usually unbranched, thick and bear cigar-shaped flowers.

Flower colour: Flower buds are a reddish-pink colour, while open flowers turn creamy white.

Flowering time: Late winter to spring.

Distribution: The species occurs in the Eastern Cape and further to the west, in the Little Karoo.

Notes: The combination of the large, blue-green rosettes[G] and the robust, bi-coloured inflorescences[G] makes this a very attractive species to grow in warmer, subtropical areas.

Lebombo aloe

Aloe spicata

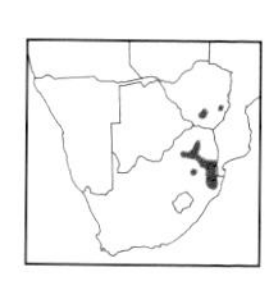

Afrikaans name: Lebombo-aalwyn

Characteristics: Plants grow as large, single- or multi-stemmed shrubs that can reach a height of two metres. The stems are clothed in old leaves. The long leaves curve snake-like, giving plants a decidedly unkempt appearance. The leaf margins are armed with small, sharp teeth. The unbranched inflorescences[G] bear large numbers of nearly stalkless flowers tightly packed on medium to tall stems.

Flower colour: Golden yellow.

Flowering time: Mid- to late winter.

Distribution: The species has a very wide distribution range in the eastern parts of northern South Africa in the Mpumalanga and Limpopo provinces.

Notes: Leaves of *Aloe spicata* are a deep reddish purple. This character is retained in cultivation if the plants are planted in full sun. Inflorescences[G] look like thin, spiky bottle-brushes because the flowers are so densely arranged on the racemes[G].

Coral aloe

Aloe striata

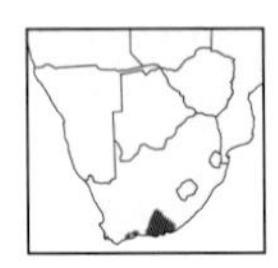

Afrikaans names: blouaalwyn, koraalaalwyn, streepaalwyn

Characteristics: Plants are solitary and stemless, but in very old specimens they could form short, creeping stems covered in the decaying remains of dry leaves. Leaves are arranged in large open rosettes[G] that are tilted to one side. The boat-shaped leaves are bluish green, which contrasts sharply with the smooth, pink leaf edges. Inflorescences[G] are heavily branched, usually flat-topped and laxly to densely flowered.

Flower colour: Bright orange.

Flowering time: Late winter to spring.

Distribution: Very common in the southern and Eastern Cape.

Notes: The general appearance of *Aloe striata* differs considerably from that of most aloes: the leaves are turquoise in colour and the leaf margins lack teeth. It is very easy in cultivation and will tolerate rain at any time of the year. In its natural habitat, hillsides covered in *Aloe striata* are an unforgettable sight.

Table Mountain aloe

Aloe succotrina

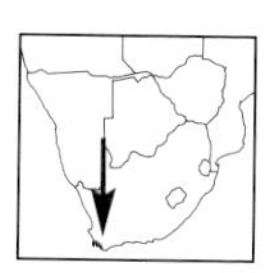

Afrikaans names: Tafelbergaalwyn, bergaalwyn

Characteristics: Plants are robust shrubs with large, rounded canopies. The central stem is short and supports a mass of stems. Each stem carries a cluster of long, erect, dull grey leaves. Leaf margins bear short, triangular, white teeth. The simple inflorescences[G] rarely have only one branch, and can reach one metre in height. The elongated flowers are thin.

Flower colour: Flower buds are bright red while the open flowers tend to be yellowish, but since only a few flowers are open at a time, inflorescences[G] appear uniformly red.

Flowering time: Late winter.

Distribution: The species is restricted to the mountains of the extreme southwestern Cape, mostly around Cape Town and neighbouring towns.

Notes: An interesting and unique feature of this aloe is that its leaves turn a distinctive purple colour when dry. This is a very rewarding species to grow in winter-rainfall areas.

Book aloe

Aloe suprafoliata

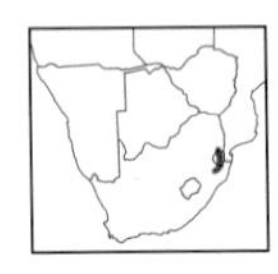

Afrikaans name: boekaalwyn

Characteristics: Plants are solitary and stemless. When plants are young, the leaves are arranged in a fan-shape, and in spirally twisted rosettes[G] as they grow older. The leaves of young plants are usually strongly recurved but tend to grow more horizontally in older plants. Leaf surfaces are bluish to purplish green, tinted with red, and unspotted. The leaf margins are armed with sharp, reddish-brown teeth. The inflorescences[G] are unbranched, and the racemes[G] conical to elongated. The thin, long flowers are pencil-shaped.

Flower colour: Varies from deep pink to bright red.

Flowering time: Mid-winter.

Distribution: The species grows in northern KwaZulu-Natal and eastern Swaziland, just entering Mpumalanga.

Notes: This species is remarkably cold-tolerant and does well in cultivation, but care should be taken to protect it from the aloe snout beetle, which seems particularly fond of it.

Aloe vera

Aloe vera

Afrikaans name: medisyne-aalwyn

Characteristics: Plants are stemless and suckering[G], producing large clumps of rosettes[G] with erect leaves. The soft leaves are spotted when young, but lose some of the spots at maturity. Leaf margins are armed with short, triangular teeth. Inflorescences[G] have one or two branches and are densely flowered.

Flower colour: Bright yellow, rarely orange or red.

Flowering time: Late winter and spring.

Distribution: The species is probably native to Arabia, but today it is grown all over the world, including in South Africa.

Notes: The medicinal properties of this species have been known for many centuries, even in biblical times. This truly domesticated aloe is grown as a garden or windowsill plant in many parts of the world, making leaf material readily accessible for treating burns and skin abrasions. Extracts of the leaf juices are also popular in health drinks and in shampoos. This is the only species of *Aloe* for which the scientific name is the same as the common name! This is a clear indication of its wide popularity in innumerable households across the world.

Blue spotted aloe

Aloe verdoorniae

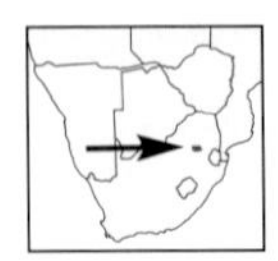

Afrikaans name: blou-bontaalwyn

Characteristics: Plants usually grow as single rosettes[G]. Multi-headed clumps are only rarely encountered. The bluish-green leaves are broadly triangular. Leaf surfaces may be adorned with white spots, particularly on the upper surface, or they lack markings entirely. Leaf margins bear short, brownish teeth. The inflorescences[G] are branched – each branch supports a conical raceme[G]. Flowers have basal swellings typical of the flowers of most spotted aloes.

Flower colour: Red – ranges from light pink with longitudinal stripes to uniformly crimson.

Flowering time: Mid-winter.

Distribution: The species occurs in a narrow band from northeastern Gauteng to Mpumalanga.

Notes: The blue-leaved plants are some of the most beautiful of all the spotted aloes. Some forms of this species can easily be confused with other spotted aloes.

Grass aloe

Aloe verecunda

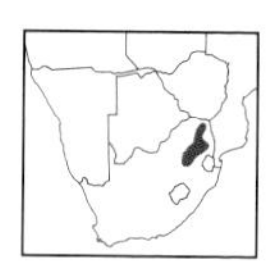

Afrikaans name: grasaalwyn

Characteristics: Plants grow as solitary or densely massed, grass-like tufts. The rosettes[G] consist of clusters of thin, erect, bright green leaves that often die in winter. Leaf margins carry small, white, harmless teeth. Especially the basal parts of the leaves are adorned with numerous small white spots. Flowers are fairly densely and tightly arranged in small, head-shaped clusters.

Flower colour: Bright red.

Flowering time: Mid- to late summer.

Distribution: This species grows in protected rock crevices on the climatically severe Highveld of South Africa, and in scattered colonies in Mpumalanga and in the Limpopo Province.

Notes: Grass aloes are generally more difficult to cultivate than most other species of *Aloe*. Part of the reason may be that their roots are often very squat and large – they require more root space than generally allowed for plants that grow no taller than about half a metre.

Wickens' aloe

Aloe wickensii

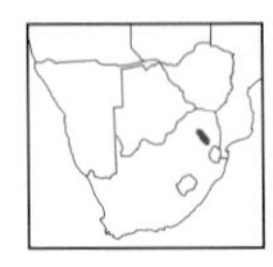

Afrikaans name: none recorded

Characteristics: Plants are stemless and unbranched, producing medium to large rosettes[G] with yellow or grey-green leaves. Leaves are borne erectly but tend to curve inwards, over-arching the center of the rosettes[G]. The leaf margins are armed with small, sharp, blackish-brown teeth. Inflorescences[G] are branched into numerous racemes[G], which bear a terminal cluster of flowers. The cone-shaped racemes[G] are generally shorter than those of *Aloe cryptopoda,* with which it may be confused.

Flower colour: Flower buds are dark red, while open flowers are yellow. *Aloe wickensii* var. *lutea* (illustrated here) has uniformly yellow flowers.

Flowering time: Mid-winter.

Distribution: The species is fairly common near Polokwane, Chunies Poort and Potgietersrust in the Limpopo Province, and near Burgersfort in Mpumalanga.

Notes: *Aloe wickensii* looks similar to *Aloe cryptopoda* and the recent trend has been to treat these two aloes as one species. However, *Aloe wickensii* is a slightly smaller plant and the typical form always has bi-coloured inflorescences[G].

Spotted aloe

Aloe zebrina

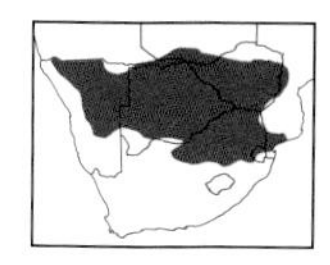

Afrikaans name: bontaalwyn

Characteristics: Plants are small and low growing. In time, they form extensive clumps through the production of side-shoots. The thick and succulent leaves are triangular in outline. Their margins are armed with very sharp, brownish teeth. Leaf surfaces are a dull green colour and spotted with irregular, egg-shaped, white spots. The flowers with their bulbous basal swellings are loosely arranged on the branches of medium to tall inflorescences[G].

Flower colour: Varies from dull pinkish to a light orange.

Flowering time: Mid- to late summer.

Distribution: This species has a wide distribution in northern South Africa and occurs in most of the neighbouring countries.

Notes: Should you encounter a summer-flowering spotted aloe on South Africa's climatically severe Witwatersdrand, it is sure to be *Aloe zebrina*. This species is a common component of the northern grassveld and bushveld regions of the country. This is the first flowering aloe to be encountered by tourists who fly to Johannesburg in the summer months.

Glossary

Basal sucker: Small plant arising from the base of a plant, resulting in genetically identical offspring; forms a small colony in time.

Bract: Leaf-like structures at the base of flowers or inflorescences.

Candle: *See* raceme.

Horticulture: The art and science of cultivating plants in a garden or landscape.

Hybrid: An animal or plant that is the offspring of two different species.

Indigenous: Describes species that occur naturally in a given area.

Inflorescence: Any arrangement of flowers into a cluster or clusters.

Raceme: A specific type of inflorescence where the flowers are arranged consecutively along a single axis and where the oldest flowers occur lowest on the axis.

Rosette: The structure in which the leaves of the vast majority of *Aloe* species are arranged, where they radiate from the crown of the plant.

Stamen: Male reproductive organs that produce pollen.

Suckering: The process by which some species of *Aloe* multiply by forming basal suckers.

Aloe chabaudii *var.* chabaudii

Photographic credits

All photographs taken by GF Smith, except for the following:

A Romanowski: p. 30.
AE van Wyk & S Malan: p. 55.
ER Fuls p. 16 (inflorescence).
Gerhard Dreyer/Struik Image Library: cover, middle left (Quiver tree).
NR Crouch: p. 43 (plant), p. 45 (plant).
P Joffe: p. 15 (inflorescence).
RR Klopper: p. 31.